This book belongs to

_____

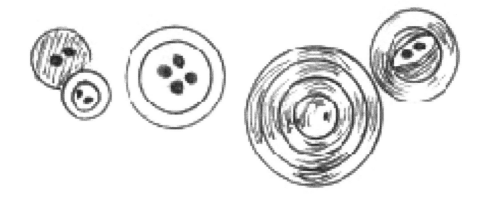

Claire's Closet

For Maple
Love, Grammy Sammy

Claire's Closet

Text copyright © 2021 by Debra Scala Giokas
Illustrations copyright © 2021 by Mary Ryan Reeves

ISBN 978-1-7367254-2-9

CHANDELIER
STREET

Chandelier Street
New York

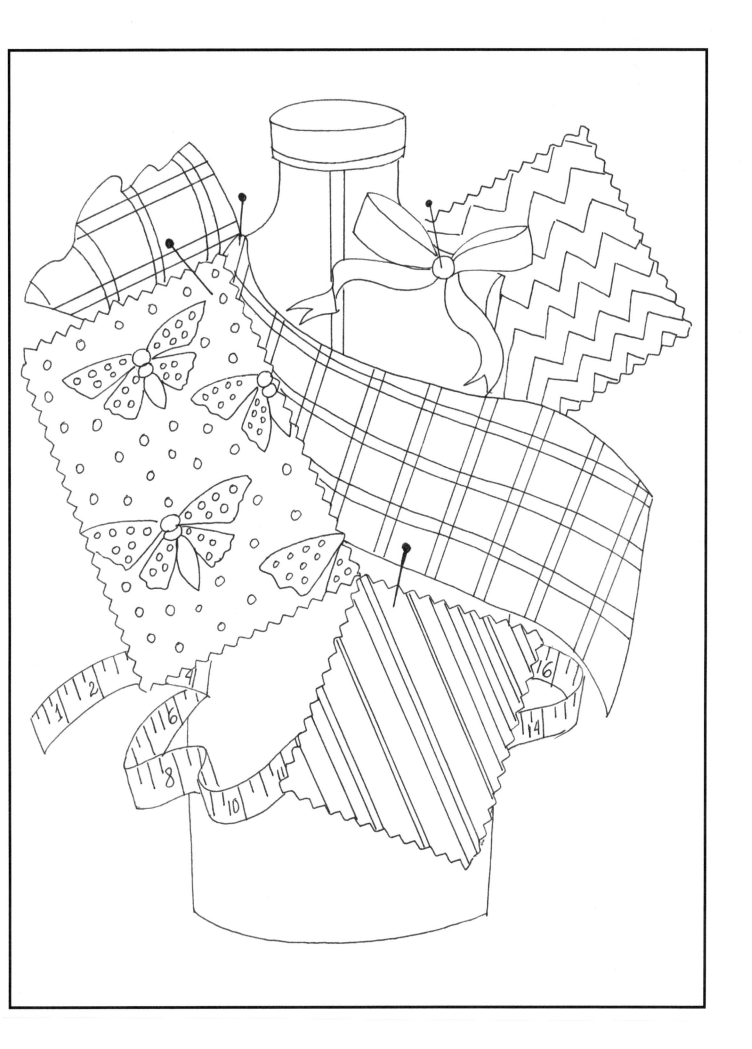

Claire McCardell is an American fashion icon.

She was born in 1905, and she changed the way women dress.

Claire wanted women to be comfortable
so they could play sports
and solve the world's problems.

She loved pockets, bows and buttons,
and fabrics of cotton, denim and wool.

She made ski caps and hooded jerseys
and ballet flats, too.

Step into Claire's closet and her imagination
and color your own wardrobe
while you learn about Claire's life and style.

You will see how her comfortable clothes live on
in the closets of today.

May you find this SEW interesting!

The description of each picture
is on the back.

Whenever you reach into your pockets,
think of Claire.

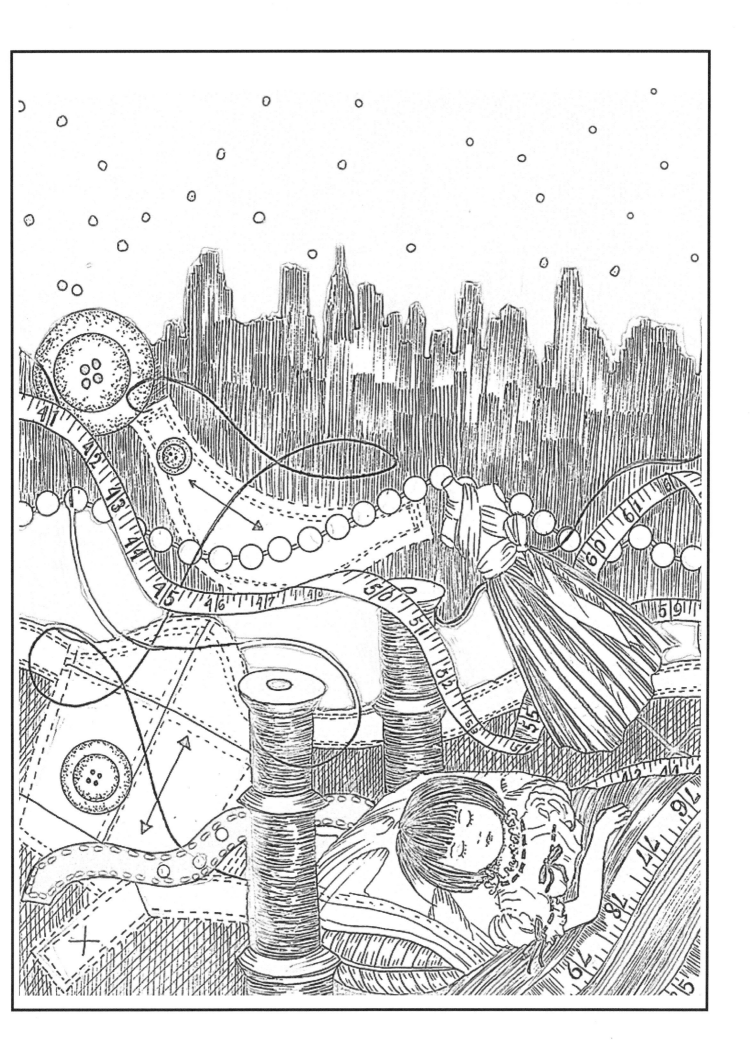

When she was a little girl, Claire McCardell had big dreams.
She wanted to study fashion design in New York City.

Claire watched Annie, her family's seamstress, make dresses.
Claire practiced her design ideas using paper dolls.

You can trace
this paper doll
and her clothing.
Then cut them out
and mix and match
like Claire did!

Claire took apart the clothes for her paper dolls,
and she mixed and matched them to make the outfits look better.

Have you ever
thought about
designing
your own line
of clothing?

CUT
OUT

Claire used her ideas from paper dolls.
When she grew up, she made real clothes.

Claire thought corsets took away freedom. They were too tight.

Claire designed the Monastic Dress in 1938.
It tied around the waist like a monk's robe.
And it was comfortable and is still in style.

Claire's Kitchen Dress had a built-in apron.
That was in 1941.

Designed in 1942, Claire's Popover Dress had a pocket for a potholder.
She loved to add pockets because they had a purpose.
Her award-winning Popover Dress was grey. What color will yours be?

Claire loved bows,
and she used them wherever she could.
Bows are still fashionable for today's modern woman.

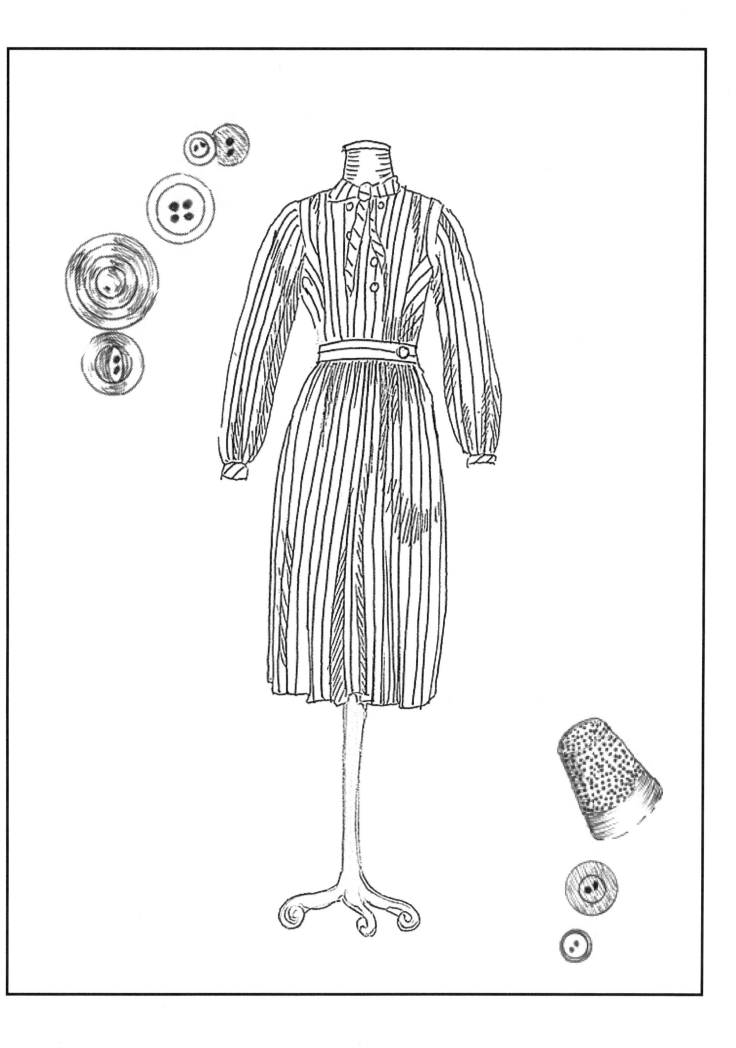

Claire designed comfortable and timeless clothes.
She loved buttons.

claire mcCardell clothes

Claire didn't use zippers. Another bow!
She had her own label, too!

Claire made practical and beautiful clothes.
They looked like they were custom made, also known as *couture*.

A classic coat with buttons. Color it your favorite.

Claire designed comfortable clothes so women could play sports and do many other things, too. What do you like to do?

"Sports clothes changed our lives
because they changed our thinking
about clothes. Perhaps they, more than
anything else, made us independent women."

~ Claire McCardell

Claire is credited with designing sportswear.
Her influence can still be felt today.

Claire invented the idea of separates so she could pack lightly on her trips and look like she had many different outfits by mixing and matching.

Claire loved to ski and designed knit caps.
She also designed hooded jerseys.

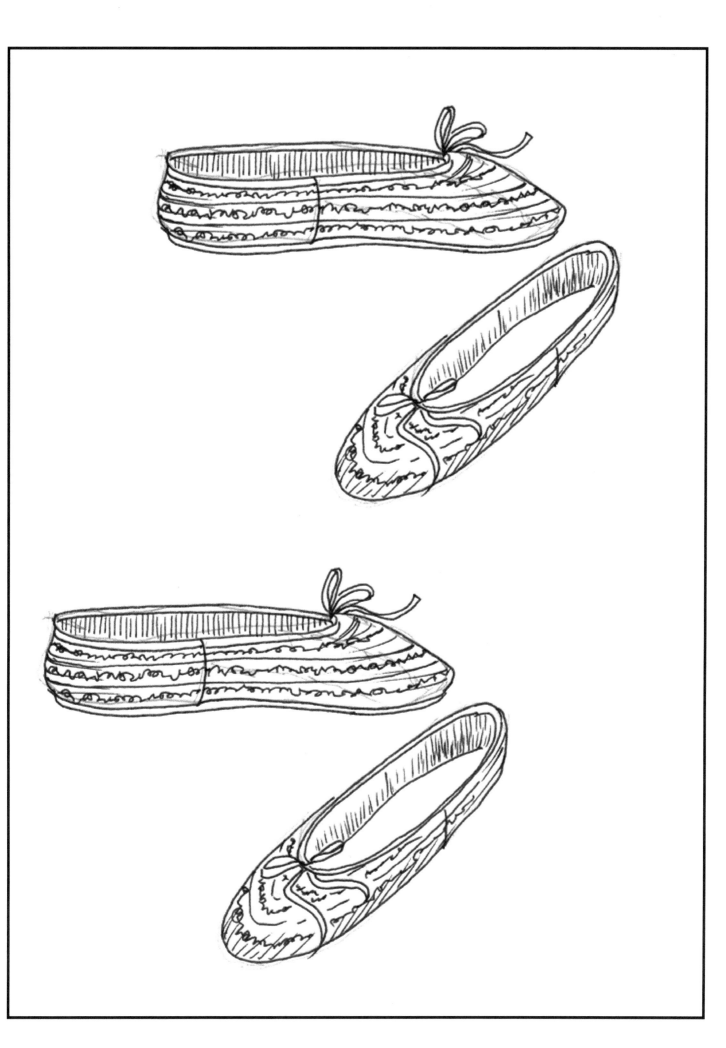

Claire created the ballet flat so women could rest their feet from high heels. What is your favorite color ballet flat?

Claire changed the way women dress forever.
"Casual never means careless," Claire said.

Claire McCardell is an American fashion icon. Claire's style continues to influence the clothes of girls and women today.
This is called the American Look.

"Casual Never Means Careless."

~ Claire McCardell

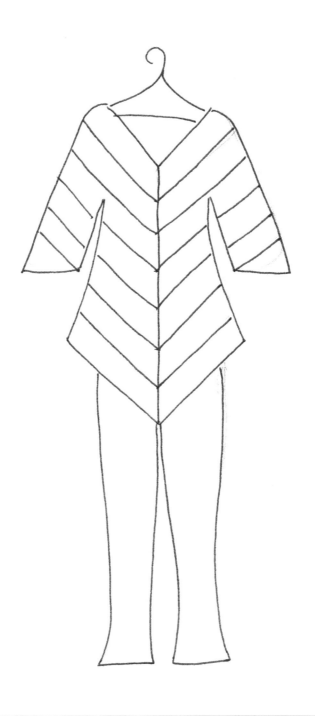

Whenever you reach into your pockets, think of Claire.
And always remember to follow your dreams.

Also illustrated by Mary Ryan Reeves,
this picture book will help you learn more about Claire McCardell.

claire

**The little girl who climbed to the top
and changed the way women dress**

words by **Debra Scala Giokas**
pictures by **Mary Ryan Reeves**

CPSIA information can be obtained
at www.ICGtesting.com
Printed in the USA
LVHW071401240521
688337LV00015B/287

9 781736 725429